Secrets
and
Surprises

S0-BEV-170

Marion Hedquist

A Beka Book® Pensacola, FL 32523-9100
an affiliate of PENSACOLA CHRISTIAN COLLEGE®

Contents

Part 1—LET'S GO!

Stories

Poems

Secrets and Surprises

Staff Credits
Edition Editor: M. Hedquist
Cover Designer: Michelle Johnson
Illustrators: Frank Hicks, Brian Jekel, Sonya Wilson

Copyright © mmv, mcmxciv Pensacola Christian College
All rights reserved. Printed in U.S.A. 2009 C08

No part of this publication may be reproduced or transmitted in any form or by any means, electronic or mechanical, including photocopy, recording, or any information storage and retrieval system, or by license from any collective or licensing body, without permission in writing from the publisher.

Cataloging Data
Hedquist, Marion
    Secrets and Surprises / by Marion Hedquist; 192 p.: col ill.; 23 cm. + teacher's
    ed. (A Beka reading program)
    1. Readers (Elementary. 2. Reading (Elementary). III. A Beka Book, Inc.
Library of Congress: PE1119 .H32 2005
Dewey System: 428.6 Hed

Phonics Charts 8 and 9

thr in three
ar in stars
ch in church
or in morning
ou in out
ow in owl
ow in bowl
er in verse
ur in nurse
ir in bird
oi in coin
oy in boy

oo in book
oo in tooth
wor in worms
igh in night
all in ball
alk in walk
-ing in pointing
kn in knot
gn in gnat

ang in bang
ing in king
ong in long
ung in strung
ank in bank
ink in wink
onk in honk
unk in trunk
wa in wash
a in adopt
y in baby
le in little
-ed in wanted
-ed in looked
-ed in played

Part 2
MEET BETH AND BRAD

Stories

Poems

Phonics Chart 10

wh in whale	-y in rainy
wh in who	-er in bigger
tch in patch	-est in biggest
ear in ear	-ly in slowly
ear in bear	-en in sharpen
ear in earth	-es in peaches
old in gold	ild in child
mb in lamb	ind in kind
ew in flew	
ew in few	

Part 3
ANIMAL ADVENTURES

Stories

Poems

Phonics Chart 11

o in shovel	ea in thread	ch in chorus
a in banana	ea in steak	ought in thought
c in city	ie in brownie	aught in caught
au in faucet	ey in key	g in giant
aw in saw	ey in obey	dge in fudge
ea in leaf	ph in phone	

zoo farm beach for

too start such know

look   better

PART 1
Let's Go!

Let's go to the farm,
Let's go to the zoo,
Let's go to the pond,
And to the beach, too.

Let's look for a lion,
Let's find a fat frog.
Let's hunt for a crab—
Better not take the dog!

Such a time we will have!
Lots of fun, I know.
I can't wait to start—
So please—*let's go!*

—*M. Hedquist*

Sight words: **have** **of**

Advanced words: **lion** **find**
(Advanced words contain special
sounds that have not yet been taught.)

playing　　falling　　swimming　　splashing
straying　　calling　　jumping　　barking

At the Pond

One fish swimming,

one boy playing,

one frog jumping,

one dog straying.

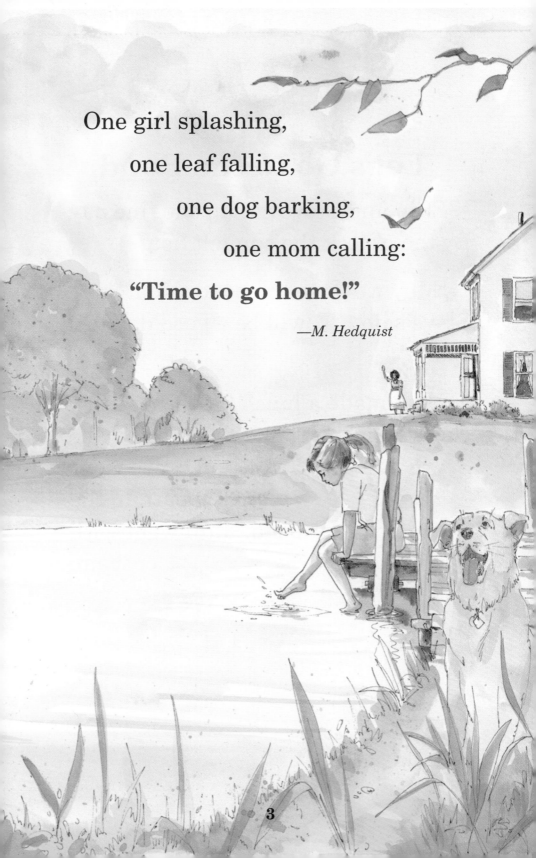

One girl splashing,

one leaf falling,

one dog barking,

one mom calling:

"Time to go home!"

—*M. Hedquist*

3

Let's Go to the Pond

Fran and Steve got up one fine day. By ten o'clock the sun felt hot.

"May we go to the pond, Mom?" Steve said. "It will be a good day to wade."

Mom made a lunch for them with cheese, crackers, and fruit. Then she, Fran, and Steve went up the path to the pond. Ruff went with them.

good   lunch   cheese
crackers   along

"Sh," Steve said to Ruff. "You must be still."

"Do you see the fish splashing, Steve? And look at that big frog," cried Fran.

The frog sat on a stone. Fran ran up to him. "Jump, frog, jump!" Fran said.

_____

look

Sight word: **do**

Think and answer: What season of the year do you think it is: spring, summer, fall, or winter?

The plump frog did not jump.
"This frog can't jump," said Fran.
"He is much too big."

"Let's get the frog," Steve said.
"Let's take it home for Dad to see."

much

"Come, frog," said Fran. "Please let me get you. Please do not jump into the pond."

Hop. Stop. Hop. Stop. The plump frog did jump!

"Please stop!" said Steve. But the frog did not stop. Plop, plop, plop! it went right into the pond.

<hr />

right

Advanced word: **come**

"Well, well," said Fran. "That frog can jump! It can jump fast. Let's try to get him."

Fran and Steve got into the wa/ter. It was fun to chase the frog. Hop. Stop. Hop, hop, plop, splash!

At last, Fran, Steve, Mom, and Ruff left the pond and the frog. It was time to go home.

---

water   **chase**

Sight word: **was**

"I like to play at the pond," Steve said.

"Yes," said Fran. "Playing tag with a frog is fun!"

Five Little
Ducks

Five little ducks went swimming one day,
 Over the pond and far away.
Mama Duck said, "Quack, quack, quack,"
And four little ducks came swimming back.

Four little ducks went swimming one day
 Over the pond and far away.
Mama Duck said, "Quack, quack, quack,"
And three little ducks came swimming back.

Three little ducks went swimming one day
 Over the pond and far away.
Mama Duck said, "Quack, quack, quack,"
And two little ducks came swimming back.

Two little ducks went swimming one day
 Over the pond and far away.
Mama Duck said, "Quack, quack, quack,"
And one little duck came swimming back.

---

far **little** o/ver a/way **three**

Sight words: **Mama** **four**

One little duck went swimming one day
    Over the pond and far away.
Mama Duck said, "Quack, quack, quack,"
And no little duck came swimming back.

Mama Duck went swimming one day
    Over the pond and far away.
Mama Duck said, "Quack, quack, quack,"
And five little ducks came swimming back!

Quack   back   quack   quack   back

Pond Fun

Match the picture with the sentence.

Steve and Fran play tag with the frog.

See the fish jump!

The plump frog jumps into the pond.

Steve, Fran, Mom, and Ruff go back home.

beach   high   stood   soaking

pinch   right   cool   pretending

might   zoo   asking

Let's Go to the Beach!

Tom went to the beach one day. He rode in the van with Mom and Dad, and his pal Mike came, too.

"This will be fun!" Tom said. "We can swim all day. I like to go swimming!"

"Please stop the van, Dad!" Tom said. "This looks like a good spot to swim."

Tom got out of the van and stood on the hot blacktop.

"Ow! That blacktop is hot," he cried. "I can't stand here. It's too hot for my feet. Let's run to the sand."

Tom and Mike ran back and forth on the beach.

"The seashore is so much fun, Tom," Mike said. "I like to feel the hot sun and the cool breeze." He stood on the sand soaking up the rays of the sun.

"I like to run into the water!" Tom said, and he ran into the waves. Mike ran in after him.

The waves were not high today.

ow   forth   cool   soaking   high

Sight word: **were**

14

The boys had fun running in and out of the water playing tag. Just then Tom felt a little bump on his leg. What was that?

"Look, Mike!" Tom cried. "Do you see what I see?"

Mike said, "Yes! I can see three little fish right here by my legs. Did one of them bump you?"

"Yes," Tom said, "but it did not bite." He began to giggle. "It felt funny."

running   right   giggle   funny
Advanced word: **what**

15

The boys ran out of the water onto the beach.

"Look, Mike," Tom cried. "Look at that crab. See the funny way he runs! I'm glad I don't run like that. He goes sideways." Tom got up close for a good look.

"Get back a little, Tom," Mike said. "He might pinch you."

The boys ran back down the beach sideways, pretending to be crabs.

out   might   pinch
down   pre/tend/ing

At last it is time to go home.

"I hate to leave the beach," Tom said. "It has been a lot of fun."

"I am glad I came with you," said Mike. "Thank you for asking me. Maybe next week you can go to the zoo with me!"

Sight word: **been**

Think and answer: Do you think Tom and Mike are good friends?

Beach Fun

Look at the pictures. In the boxes beside the pictures, put a 1, 2, or 3 to show what happened first, second, and third in the story.

Jesus Sees Me

Jesus sees me
When I sleep.

Jesus sees me
When I play.

Jesus sees me
All the time,

Every night and
Every day!

Sight word: **every**

Advanced word: **when**

down wooden empty

Advanced words: **they sandy could**

At the Sea

When I was down beside the sea,
A wooden spade they gave to me
   To dig the sandy shore.
My holes were empty like a cup;
In every hole the sea came up
   Till it could come no more.

—Robert Louis Stevenson

20

Let's Go to the Zoo!

Mike's dad took Tom and Mike to the zoo. They all rode in a pickup truck.

See the boys jump out! They will see so much today.

"Let's run to the gate," Mike said. "I can't wait to see all the animals!"

Advanced word: **an/i/mals**

took boys out

Mike's dad gave cash to the boys, and the boys paid the man at the gate.

"Let's walk on this path first," Mike's dad said. "I think I can see an el/e/phant!"

walk   **first**   **think**   Advanced word: **el/e/phant**

"Yes, I see him too," Mike spoke up. "Look at his trunk. He is as big as a house!"

"Well, maybe not a house, but he is big," Mike's dad said with a grin.

The boys came to a pond next.

"I can see a big, gray animal," Mike cried out. "I do not know what it is. Do you know what kind of animal that is, Tom?"

Tom got up close to the rail. He got a good look at the big animal. "No, Mike, I have not seen an animal like this before. But I am glad my nose is not that big!"

trunk

Advanced word: **what**

Just then the big gray animal stood up. He made a loud noise.

"What is this animal?" Mike said to his dad. "Do you know?"

"Yes, I do. It is a hip/po/pot/a/mus," Dad said.

Mike tried to say *hippopotamus*. "I can't say that!" Mike said.

"Well, we can make a short name for him. You can call him a hip/po," his dad said.

"Look at his mouth," Tom cried. "See the big teeth! What a big toothbrush he must use!"

---

stood   loud   noise   short
call   mouth   tooth/brush
Advanced word: **hip/po/pot/a/mus**

The boys ran down the path. Tom saw a big pen.

The pen had a tree in it and a black animal.

Advanced word: **saw**

"Do you see what I see?" Tom said to Mike.

"Yes, it is a mon/key!" Mike said. "See him run and jump on the tree. I will stand close to the pen. I hope he will see me. I'm going to try to reach him with my hand."

"Look out, Mike!" Tom cried. "He might hit your hand. I am glad he cannot reach you."

---

going   reach

Sight word: **your**   Advanced word: **monkey**

"No, Tom. He will not hurt me," Mike said. "He sees his ball on the path. I will get his ball for him. It will be fun to play ball with a monkey."

hurt   ball

"I see a tall animal," Mike's dad said. "See the long neck God gave him."

"Oh, my," cried Mike. "I hope he will not get a sore throat! It will hurt a lot."

"See what the giraffe can do with his long neck," said Tom. "He can eat the leaves right off the trees."

"We must go soon," said Mike's dad, "But let's go down this path first."

"See the big cat sleep in the sun on that rock," Tom cried. "It is a tiger!"

---

long　　**tall**　　**soon**

Sight word: **oh**　　　　　　　Advanced word: **giraffe**

"Yes," Mike said, "I like his black stripes. He looks like my cat at home. But I don't think I will try to play with this cat. He is not tame."

The boys got into the truck. They were tired, but it had been a good day. They had a lot to talk about.

"I am glad you took me to the zoo," Tom said. "I am glad I got to see all the animals God made."

---

talk   a/bout

contraction: **don't = do not**   Advanced word: **they**

Think and answer:
1. Why do you think God may have given the tiger black stripes?
2. Did God make *all* of the animals in the world?

Zoo Fun

Color just the five animals that Mike and Tom saw at the zoo. Then number those five animals 1, 2, 3, 4, 5 in the order that the boys saw them at the zoo.

lion

kangaroo

tiger

hippopotamus

monkey

giraffe

elephant

zebra

33

Dad

Mike's dad is big,
And Bill's dad is small.
Chad's dad has whiskers
And is six feet tall!

Mike's dad takes us to the zoo.
Bill's dad likes to play ball.
But my dad belongs to *me*,
And he's the *best* dad of all!

—M. Hedquist

small   **be/longs**

Advanced word: **whiskers**

Going to the Farm

May I ride the horse?
May I milk the cow?
(If I miss the can,
Will you show me how?)

May I take water
And grain to the hen?
(I'll run by the pig—
It stinks in his pen!)

I love the farm!
I wish Dad would say,
"We're not going home,
We're here to stay!"

—*M. Hedquist*

horse   show   cow   how   water   stinks

Contraction: **we're = we are**   Advanced words: **love   would**

Let's Go to the Farm!

Barb ran into the house. She held a card in her hand. It had come in the mailbox.

"Mom, please read the card," Barb said. "May we go to the farm? Grandma wants to see us! May we go next week? Please?"

Mom had a big smile. "We will ask Dad," she said. "I think he will say we can go."

At last the big day came.

Mom, Dad, Barb, and Spot drove all day long. Barb sang songs until Spot began to howl. He was trying to sing too!

"Let's play a word game," Dad said. "Look for something that begins with the letter *a*, then *b*, then *c*, all the way to *z*."

It was fun playing games in the car.

At last they got to the farm, and Barb got out of the car. She was glad to be at the farm at last.

"Look at Spot," Barb said. "He is glad to be here, too. See him jump out of the back seat. Look at him run and chase his tail."

---

sang   songs   howl   trying   sing

word   letter   playing   car

Advanced word: **something**

Think and answer: Is Grandma's farm near Barb's house?

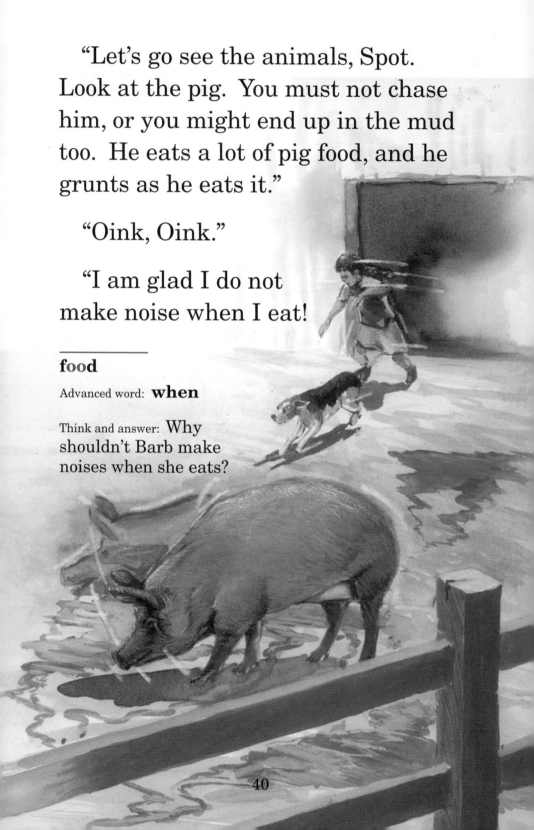

"Let's go see the animals, Spot. Look at the pig. You must not chase him, or you might end up in the mud too. He eats a lot of pig food, and he grunts as he eats it."

"Oink, Oink."

"I am glad I do not make noise when I eat!

---

food

Advanced word: **when**

Think and answer: Why shouldn't Barb make noises when she eats?

"Look at the cow, Spot. She is brown. You must not chase her."

"We can get good milk from her. I like to pat her. She is so soft!"

---

brown

Advanced word: **from**

41

"Look at the hen, Spot. You must not chase her. See her pecking at the grain Grandpa left in the barnyard for her. She likes to eat it. She must be a good mother. She keeps her baby chicks with her all the time. Soon she will lay an egg. Maybe Grandma will fix ham and eggs. Yum!"

pecking   barnyard   baby   chicks

Advanced words: **Grandpa**   **mother**   **Grandma**

"Look at all the sheep in the pen, Spot. I can count nine of them. You must not chase them. I like to feel the wool on the sheep's back. Did you hear the sheep bleat? That is how he talks to his wife!"

count   wool   how

"See the pond, Spot. Is that a duck
on the water? Maybe she will swim
by us, but you must not chase her.

"Oh, look! She has baby ducks
with her. How cute!"

"I am tired, Spot. It has been a
long day, our first day at the farm. I
am glad we will be here a week."

"We have a lot more
to see yet. Grandma
said that one of the
barn cats had kittens.
Dad said that we
can do jobs, too.
It will be fun
to do jobs
at the farm."

―――――
our

44

"In the morning I will feed the pigs and the chickens. Maybe I can take grain to the cows, too. I will work hard so Dad can be proud of me. Then I will go for a short ride on the horse.

"Wait! I hear a dog barking. It must be Spot. No, no, Spot!"

work   proud   horse   morn/ing

"You must not chase the hen. She will not like it, and you might hurt her or one of her baby chicks. I must tie you up for now. If we do bad things, we will hurt others."

now   things

Advanced word: **oth/ers**

Farming

The farmer plants the seeds in spring
    That grow up green and tall.
His tractor helps him work the ground
    And gather crops in fall.

Animals help the farmer, too—
    A dog, a cat, a horse.
Sheep grow wool, hens lay eggs,
    And cows give milk, of course.

God helps the farmer do his work,
    For God makes all things grow.
That's why we thank God for our food.
    It comes from Him, we know.

—Janice Sherwin

farmer	spring	grow
ground	gather	fall
thank		

Sight words: **give   course**

Advanced words: **tractor   why**
from

48

Farm Helpers

*What do these animals give us? Draw lines to match.
Color the pictures.*

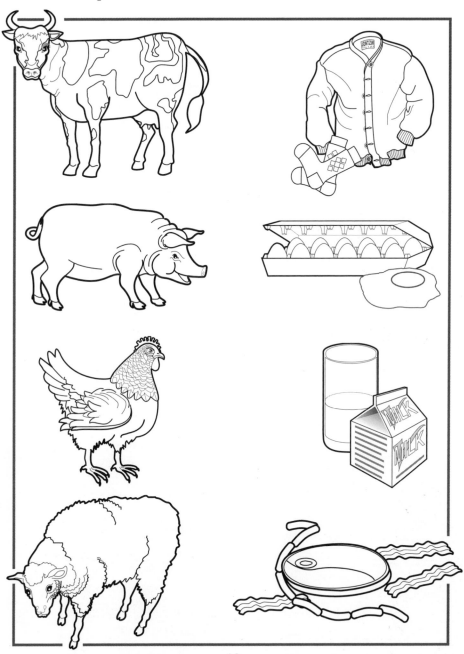

Clouds

White sheep, white sheep,
On a blue hill,
When the wind stops
You all stand still.
When the wind blows
You walk away slow.
White sheep, white sheep,
Where do you go?

—*Christina Rossetti*

---

blows   **slow**

Sight word: **where**   Advanced word: **white**

50

camping	smooth	bring	worm
fishing	hook	strung	jerk
peeking	moon	strong	sturdy

Camping

Setting up the tent,
Camping by the lake,
Fishing with a pole,
Looking for a snake!

Cooking on a fire,
Seeing Ruff's tail wag,
Peeking at the moon
From my sleeping bag.

—*M. Hedquist*

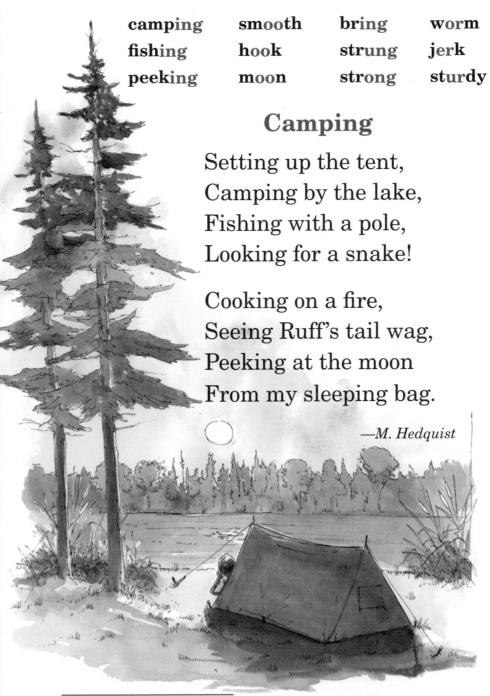

| setting | looking | cooking | seeing |
| peeking | sleeping | | Advanced word: **from** |

51

Let's Go Camping!

Dad put the tent in the back of the van and shut the door. Then Todd got into the van. He had his sleeping bag in his hand.

"This will be lots of fun, Dad! I am so glad we get to go camping."

Dad smiled, "I am glad, too!"

Advanced word: **put**

"Do we get to eat hot dogs, Dad? I like hot dogs."

"No," Dad said. "We will not eat hot dogs this time." Dad had a big grin on his face. "We will eat a meal that we get with a pole," he said.

"A pole!" Todd cried.

Todd saw his dad's grin. "Is this a joke?"

"No, it is not a joke," his dad said.

Advanced words: **face** **saw**

Just then Todd saw the fishing poles in the back of the van. He let out a squeal.

"We get to go fishing!" he cried. "Yes, this will be *lots* of fun! The last time we went fishing was in June, and this is September. I love to go fishing!"

September

Advanced word: **love**

Todd and his dad drove for a long time.

At last Todd saw the lake.

Dad said, "This is the spot. We will camp by that big tree." He drove the van close to the tree, and they got out.

Dad said, "Todd, get the fishing poles. I will get the tent."

Todd got the poles.
"May I help you with the tent, Dad?"

Todd's dad let him help. First
Todd got to pick the spot where the
ground was flat and smooth. Then
Dad let him bring the tent spikes and
help lay out the tent. Dad drove the
spikes into the ground as Todd got
the sleeping bags. Soon the tent
was up.

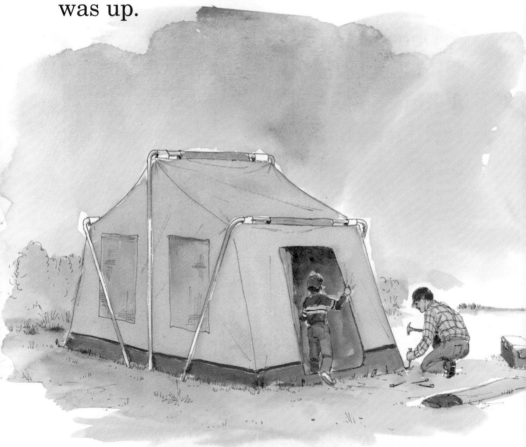

smooth   bring

"That tent is big!" Todd said. "Will it stay up?"

"Oh, yes," Dad said. "This tent is strong and sturdy. Zip up the zipper in the door, and let's go fishing!

Todd ran to get the fishing poles and bait, and off they went to the lake. Soon Todd was sitting on a tree stump with his pole.

strong   sturdy   zipper

He put a worm on his hook and put the line into the water.

Todd's dad sat on a stump by him. He said, "We must be still now, Todd."

It felt good to sit and soak up the sun.

Just then Todd felt a jerk on his line and saw a fish splash.

His dad said, "You got a bass, Todd!"

worm   hook   jerk

Advanced word: **put**

Todd cried, "It's a big one, Dad! I hope I can keep it on my line." Todd's dad came to help him.

Just then, Todd swung the line back, and the fish hit the bank by Todd.

"You got it, Todd!" his dad said.

Todd had a big grin. "May I clean it now, Dad? I can't wait to eat it!"

swung   bank

Todd got to help clean the fish, and
then it was time to pick up sticks for
the fire. Dad fried Todd's fish in a big
pan over the fire, and they ate it with
beans. That fish did taste good!

That night Todd lay in his sleeping
bag. His dad was beside him. Todd
felt good inside. It was fun to camp
with his dad. It was fun to fish in the
lake and then eat the fish. It was fun
to sleep in a tent.

Todd saw the moon peeking in the flap of the tent. Todd said, "Dad, God is good to us!"

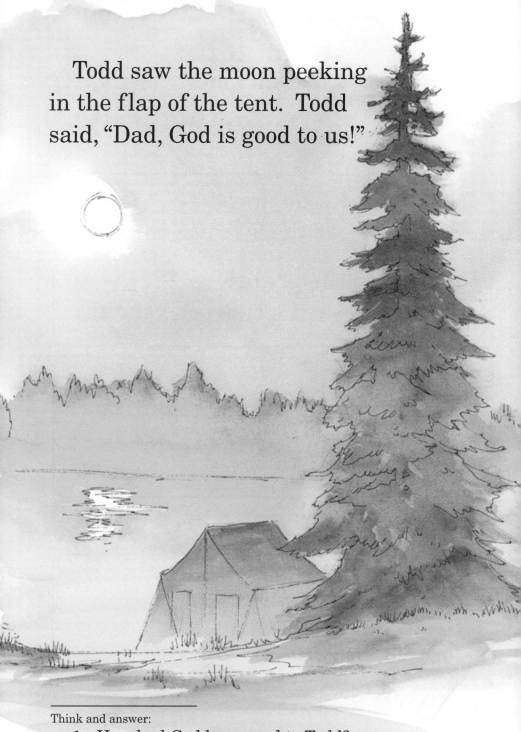

Think and answer:
1. How had God been good to Todd?
2. How has God been good to you?

Which One?

Mark the ○ by the sentence in each box that tells what happened in the story.

Dad and Todd drove
to the lake in a car. ○

Dad and Todd drove
to the lake in a van. ○

Todd got a big bass. ○

Dad got a big bass. ○

Todd ate hot dogs by the fire. ○

Todd ate fish by the fire. ○

Interstate

When Daddy doesn't
want to be late,
He drives to work
on the in/ter/state.

—*Laurel Hicks*

Daddy　　**interstate**

Contraction: **doesn't = does not**

Hey Diddle Diddle

Hey diddle diddle,
The cat and the fiddle,
The cow jumped over the moon.
The little dog laughed
To see such sport,
    And the dish ran

        away with

            the spoon.

I See the Moon

I see the moon,
    And the moon sees me;
God bless the moon,
    And God bless me.

---

diddle   **fiddle**   **jumped**   **sport**   **spoon**

Sight word: **laughed**   Advanced word: **hey**

Man in the Moon

The Man in the Moon looked
    out of the moon,
And this is what he said:
"Now that I'm getting up,
    it's time
All children went to bed."

---

looked   **getting**   **children**

Suffixes

A suffix comes at the end of the root word to make a new word. Practice these suffix words. They will be found in the following stories.

-ed

-ed in looked ("t")

thank	help	ask	check
thanked	helped	asked	checked
watch	miss	peck	peek
watched	missed	pecked	peeked

-ed in played ("d")

call	starve	agree	hug
called	starved	agreed	hugged
moan	pray	turn	curl
moaned	prayed	turned	curled

-ed in wanted ("ĕd")

count	point	start	wait
counted	pointed	started	waited

-en   -y   -ly

eat	fall	greed	near
eaten	fallen	greedy	nearly

Grandma's Glasses

Here are Grandma's glasses;
Here is Grandma's hat;
This is the way she folds her hands
And lays them in her lap.

fold   hold   gold

Here are Grandpa's glasses;
Here is Grandpa's hat;
This is the way he
    folds his arms,
Just like that.

hat   flat   splat

folds   glasses

Advanced words: **Grandma's   Grandpa's**

Beth and Brad think it's fun
   to be twins,
With two times the giggles
   and two times the grins.

wiggle   giggle

twins   grins   chins

We'll learn things with them
   about candy and birds—
Looking for the cat and
   trusting God's Words.

word   bird   third

—M. Hedquist

———
learn

Birthday Surprise

Brad and Beth are twins. Beth is a girl, and Brad is a boy. They are five right now, but soon they will be six. The twins went to kin/der/gar/ten last year, and now they can read well. They like to read 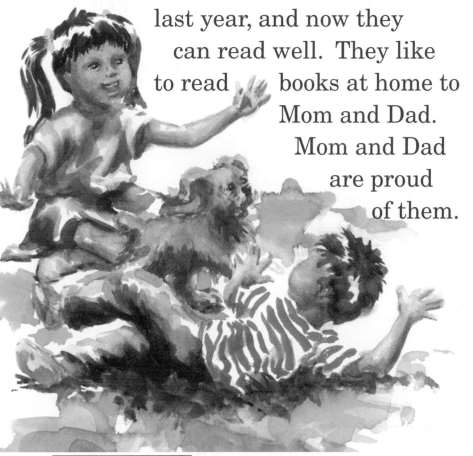 books at home to Mom and Dad. Mom and Dad are proud of them.

Think and answer: If Beth's birthday is September 6th, when is Brad's birthday?

Beth and Brad have the same birthday. Mom is going to bake them a cake in the shape of the number six. The twins can hardly wait!

At last the big day came. Just before lunch time, the doorbell rang. Ding! Dong! Brad ran to the door. The mailman had a box for the twins. It had Grandma's name in the corner.

_____
hardly

What was in the box? Was it something to wear? Was it books or a game? Mom said they must wait, but, oh, it was so hard to wait!

At last it was time to cut the cake. The twins ran to the table and waited for Mom.

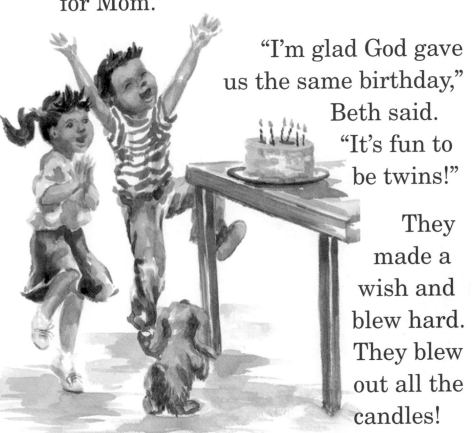

"I'm glad God gave us the same birthday," Beth said. "It's fun to be twins!"

They made a wish and blew hard. They blew out all the candles!

---

wear   **waited**   **blew**   Advanced word: **something**

Just before Mom cut the cake, they prayed. They thanked God for the cake and for making them twins. At last they got to eat birthday cake!

Ding! Dong! The doorbell rang, and Beth ran to the door this time. What a surprise!

"Grandma!" Beth cried with a grin from ear to ear. "How did you get here?"

Grandma hugged Brad and Beth.

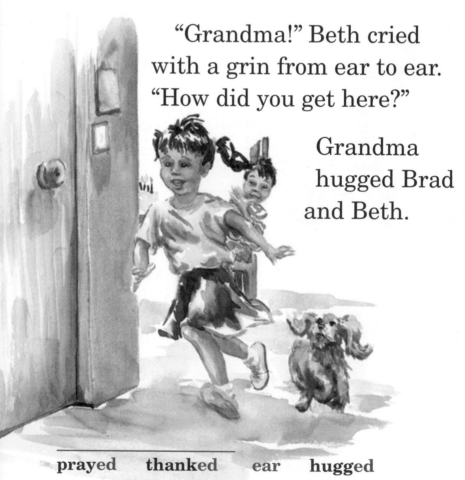

prayed   thanked   ear   hugged

"I wanted to surprise you," she said. "I came on the plane. I came to see if you like the gift I sent you for your birthday."

Beth took the bow off the box, and Brad took off the paper and the lid.

"Oh, Grandma! We do like the gift," the twins cried. The box had a lot of books in it.

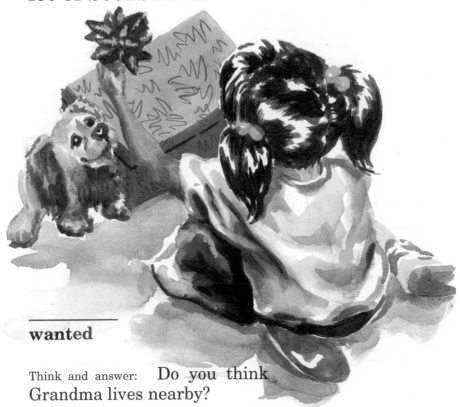

wanted

Think and answer: Do you think Grandma lives nearby?

"We love to read," Beth said. "We will read all of these books for you."

"I hope you will," Grandma said with a smile.

"I like the gift," Brad spoke up, "but the best thing we got for our birthday is *you*." And Brad stuck the bow on Grandma!

Draw a Twin

Draw an identical twin for this boy. Follow step by step to make him look just like his twin.

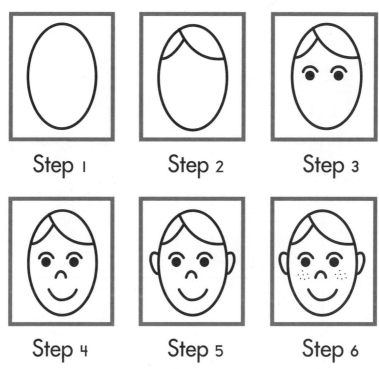

Step 1 Step 2 Step 3

Step 4 Step 5 Step 6

Draw your twin here.

Birthday Fun

Look at the pictures. Number them 1–4 in the order that things happened in the story. Put the numbers in the boxes.

76

kind   when   eaten

dear   why   greedy

Getting Too Much

Ding! Dong! Ding! Dong!

"The doorbell is ringing," Brad called.

"I will get it," Beth said, and she ran to the door. The mailman stood on the step. He had a box for Brad and Beth.

The box had Grandma's name on it.

"This box can't be for our birthday," Beth said. "We just had our birthday."

"How kind of Grandma to send us a gift! What is it for?"

"May we open the box, Mom?" Brad asked.

"Let me read the card first," Mom said.

She took the card off the side of the box. Then she read out loud,

Dear Brad and Beth,
This is an "I'm proud of you" gift.
Make it last as long as you can.
I love you.

Grandma

kind   **dear**

Advanced word: **read**

"Yes, you may open the box," Mom said. Brad and Beth tore the box open.

"Wow! Look at this," Brad cried.

The box had candy in it—lots of candy. The twins counted the candy and made two piles.

Beth said, "I am going to make my candy last for two weeks."

"I am, too," Brad a/greed.

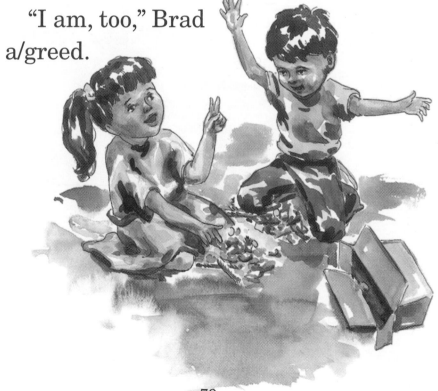

"That is wise," Mom said.

Brad took his candy to his room. He looked and looked at it. It looked so good! He chose one candy bar and ate it. Then he went to play ball.

When he came back to his room, he looked at the candy. It looked so good, and he felt starved! Brad took more candy, and then he took more. He did not stop until he had eaten all the candy!

when   eat/en

Think and answer: Why did Mom think Beth's plan was wise?

When it was time to eat supper, Brad felt sick. He did not want to eat a thing. He said, "May I go to my room and lie down? I do not feel well."

Mom looked at Brad. Then she looked at Dad and smiled. "Yes, you may go to your room," she said.

"Brad, this is shrimp!" Beth said. "It is the meal we like best!"

"Not tonight," Brad moaned. "I am sick." He got up and went to bed.

The next day, Brad felt fine. He and Beth got out bikes to go for a ride.

"Wait!" Beth said. "Let's take a candy bar with us. It will taste good when we get hot and tired."

"I can't," Brad had to tell her. "I ate all my candy."

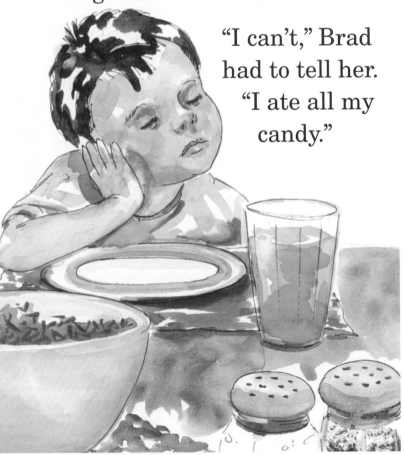

"Brad, is that why you were sick last night? Is that why you did not want to eat shrimp?"

"Yes," Brad said, "and now you will get to eat candy for two more weeks. I will not get to eat any. I wish I had been wise like you. Next time I will not be greedy!"

greedy   why

Sight word: **any**

Sentence Match

*Which picture matches the sentence? Mark the ○ under
the correct picture.*

1. The mailman came up the walk.

○   ○   ○

2. Brad and Beth are riding bikes.

○   ○   ○

few   watch   nearly
flew   whole   fallen
new   feeder

A Few Riddles with *ew*

Draw lines to match the riddle with the picture.

This baby said,
"Mew."

This baby will
chew!

This baby flew
down our street.

This baby grew
little feet.

_____

mew   chew   grew

85

Brad's Secret

"Beth, it is time to go," Brad called. Beth looked at her watch. It was nearly three o'clock.

"Here I come," Beth called. She got her purse and ran down the steps. It was time to walk to the store with Grandma.

---

nearly   watch

Grandma and Brad were waiting for Beth.

"I love to stay with you, Grandma!" Beth said. "It's fun to walk to the store on your street."

Grandma smiled. "Spring days are good days for walks," she said. "I like to see the flow/ers and the bright green leaves on the trees."

Soon they were at the door of the little store.

"What will you get, Beth?" Brad asked.

"I am going to get bird seed," Beth said.

"If you get bird seed," Brad said, "I will get yarn."

Think and answer: What things might you see if you go for a walk on a spring day?

feeder

"Yarn?" Beth asked. "Why do you want to get yarn? What will you do with it?"

Brad smiled a se/cret smile. "You will see," he said.

Beth got three bags of bird seed, and Brad got red, blue, and green yarn.

When they got home, they ran to the bird feeder in the back yard.

"I'm so glad Grandpa made this for us!" Brad said. "It will be fun to feed the birds."

"Yes," Beth said, "we can look for all kinds of birds. I like blue jays best." Then she looked at Brad. "But what will you do with the yarn?" she asked.

"You will see," Brad said with a smile.

That day the twins watched for
birds. The first bird to come to the
feeder was a robin. They liked his
red tummy. It was fun to see him
peck the seed. They saw a finch and
a blue jay, too. It did not take long
for them to see that the blue jay was
a bully. He wanted
the whole bird
feeder for
himself!

<u>whole</u>   Advanced word: **bully**

That night Brad took the yarn to his room. He cut the yarn into short pieces. He had short pieces of red, blue, and green. Then he got out a brown bag of pine cones.

He had picked up the pine cones from Grandma's yard. They had fallen from a pine tree. Now he had a way to use them. He took a few short pieces of yarn and stuck them into two pine cones.

---

fallen   Advanced word: **pieces**

The ends of the pieces of yarn hung out. Brad looked at his pine cones and smiled. They looked odd!

The next day Brad took the two pine cones to the back yard.

Just then Beth ran down the back steps. She looked at the pine cones. "What will you do with those things?" she asked.

"I will set these in the back yard," Brad said. "I think the birds will like them."

"What will the birds do with pine cones and yarn?" Beth asked. "Will they eat them?"

Brad just smiled. "You will see," he said.

Each day the twins checked the pine cones. Each day they counted the pieces of yarn.

At first just a few pieces of yarn were missing—then more and more.

Then one day they saw a robin fly down to a pine cone. With its beak it pecked at a piece of yarn. They saw the bird pull it out and fly away.

"Quick!" Brad said. "Let's see if it has a nest." They ran after the bird. The bird flew up into a little tree.

Advanced word: **pull**

"I can see the nest!" Brad cried. "Can you see it, Beth?"

Beth looked up into the tree. She saw bits of red, green, and blue.

"Yes," she said. "Now I see what the birds do with the yarn. They use it to help make a good nest. Then the bird will lay eggs in her nest."

Think and answer: Which does a bird do first, lay her eggs or build her nest? Why?

"Brad," Beth asked, "How do you think a bird knows the right way to make a nest? The nest has to be strong so that the rain will not wash it away."

"I think I know," Brad said. "I think God tells the bird how to do it. She can't read a book, so God just makes her so that she knows!"

"This has been fun, Brad. I will tell Mom that today I helped make a new red, green, and blue home right in Grandma's back yard!"

What Happened First?

Number these pictures in the order that they took place in the story.

Once I Saw a
Little Bird

Once I saw a little bird
Come hop, hop, hop,
And I cried, "Little Bird,
Will you stop, stop, stop?"

I was going to the win/dow
To say, "How do you do?"
But he shook his little tail
And away he flew.

Sight word: **once**

The Secret

We have a secret, just we three,
The robin and I, and the sweet cherry tree,—
The bird told the tree, and the tree told me,
And nobody knows it but just we three.

But of course, the robin knows best,
Because he built the—I shan't tell the rest;
And laid the four little—something in it—
I'm afraid I shall tell it every minute.

But if the tree and the robin don't peep,
I'll try my best the secret to keep;
Though I know when the little birds fly about,
Then the whole secret will be out.

—Author Unknown

---

told　　　　　　Advanced words: **cherry　because**

Sight words: **built　minute　though**

99

Puff's Surprise

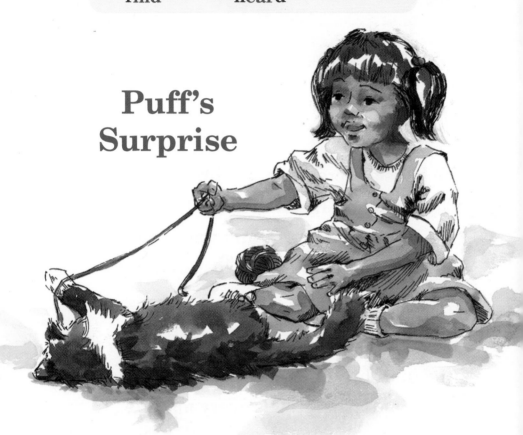

Beth was looking for her cat. "Puff, Puff!" she called.

Puff was Beth's black and white cat. Puff liked to play with Beth. She liked to chase yarn and string. She liked to play with big brown bags.

She liked to curl up by Beth and sleep. But Beth had not seen Puff all day. Beth found Brad in his room.

"Brad, have you seen Puff?" she asked. "I have not seen her all day."

"No, I haven't seen her," Brad said. "Have you looked outside?"

"I will look in the back yard," Beth said, and she ran out the door.

"Puff, Puff!" Beth called in the back yard. Then she saw something black and white.

It was in a hole under the back step. Beth ran to the hole and peeked in. Puff peeked out at her.

The next day Beth did her chores. Then she and Brad went for a bike ride.

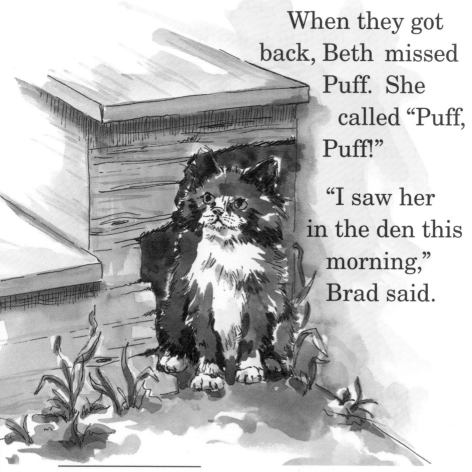

When they got back, Beth missed Puff. She called "Puff, Puff!"

"I saw her in the den this morning," Brad said.

Think and answer: What are chores? What chores might Beth do around the house?

102

"The den," Beth said. "I did not go to the den this morning. Let's see if we can find her."

The twins ran into the den.

"Puff! Are you here?" Beth called. They did not hear a sound. Beth turned on the light, and they looked all around the room.

"Here she is!" Beth called. Brad bent down and saw Puff.

She was curled up on the bot/tom shelf of a bookcase.

---

find   hear   Advanced words: **saw   bot/tom**

"Puff, why are you here?" Beth asked. She picked Puff up and took her to her room.

The next day Beth got the cat food and went to Puff's dish to feed her.

"Puff," she called, but Puff did not run to the dish today.

Beth found her mom in the kitchen.

kitchen

"Mom, Puff will not play with me," Beth said. "She hides from me in little corners. Is she mad at me?"

"No, I do not think so," Mom said. "I think she is looking for the right spot. She is planning a surprise for you." Beth told Brad about the surprise.

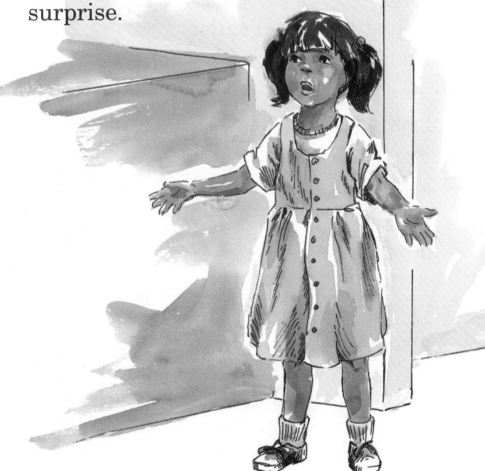

"A surprise?" Brad asked. "What kind of surprise?"

"I do not know," Beth said, "but I hope it will be a good one. I do not want her to run away."

The twins looked and called for Puff.

Just then Dad called from the basement. "Are you looking for Puff?" he asked. "She is down here."

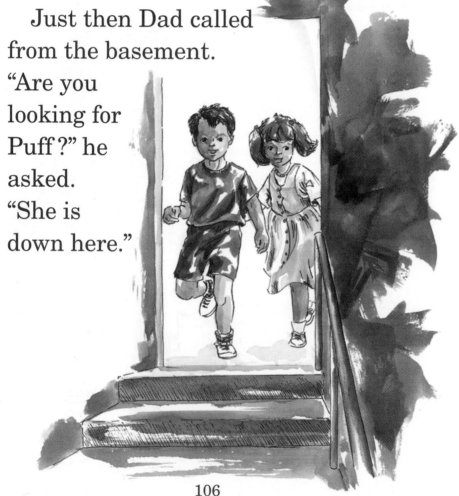

The twins ran down the steps. Dad pointed to a box in a dark corner. Beth saw Puff's green eyes shin/ing. "Puff!" she cried. "Why are you here?" She bent down to pick Puff up.

Just then Beth heard a noise. Something said, "Mew."

_____
heard

Sight word: **eyes**

"Oh, Brad!" Beth cried. "I know what Puff's surprise is! Look in the box!" In the box Brad saw three baby kittens.

"Oh, wow!" Brad said. "I like your surprise, Puff!"

And Puff looked up as if to say, "Thank you! I'm glad you like it!"

Puff's Hiding Places

Where did Puff hide? Mark the ○ under the pictures that show where Puff hid.

109

More -ed Words

Circle the right word in each sentence.

Dad had to (**park** / **parked**) the car.

The vase broke when Pam
(**drop** / **dropped**) it.

I hope it will not (**start** / **started**)
to rain.

We love to (**pray** / **prayed**) to God.

The cat (**jump** / **jumped**) into
Beth's lap.

Read these suffix words.

ed in looked		**ed in played**	
dress	rush	love	grin
dressed	rushed	loved	grinned
brush	wink	scrub	open
brushed	winked	scrubbed	opened
park	wish		
parked	wished		

Beth's Secret

Beth and Brad got in the car after church. They were both talking at once.

Beth said, "Mom, guess what we found out today!"

Brad did not wait for Mom to guess. He told her, "Mrs. Smith is going away. We will have a new teacher next week."

Sight words: **both guess Mrs.**

111

Mrs. Smith was Beth and Brad's Sunday school teacher. The twins were sad all the way home. They loved Mrs. Smith. They were going to miss her. Brad would miss Mr. Smith, too. He had helped with the class lots of times.

Dad told the twins, "Let's trust God. After all, His way is always best. Let's pray that He will send the right teacher to your class."

That week, Beth and Brad both prayed.

Sight word: **Mr.**   Advanced words: **school   would   always**

112

Sat/ur/day night, Beth heard Mom talk on the phone. She ran to find Brad.

"I know a secret!" she said with a big smile.

"Oh, Beth, tell me, tell me!" Brad cried.

"You will find out in the morning," Beth said. "And you will like the secret." She would not tell him any more.

Advanced word: **phone**

The next morning, Brad heard
Beth in her room. She was getting
dressed for Sunday school.

Brad heard Beth hum to herself.
He knew she was happy. He dropped
a shoe on his toe. Ouch! That hurt!
He wished he knew the secret, too.
Then he heard Beth start to sing.
Brad had to smile.

knew

Sight word: **shoe**

He got out his new shirt. Maybe Mom would let him wear it. He brushed his teeth and scrubbed his face till it shone.

Soon Beth and Brad were all dressed. They got their Bi/bles and got into the car.

Soon Mom and Dad came too, and they were on their way to church. Beth talked all the way.

Sight word: **their** Advanced word: **face**

Think and answer: Why did Beth and Brad take their Bibles to church?

The twins jumped out as soon as Dad parked the car. They rushed down the hall to their Sunday school class. Brad looked all around. No teacher was in sight! He looked at Beth.

She just grinned at him. Brad sat down by James. James looked around, too.

"Do you know who our new teacher is, Brad?"

"No," Brad started to say. Just then the door opened. Brad's mom walked up to the front of the class.

She looked at Beth and Brad and winked. Brad heard Beth giggle

---

Sight word: **who**

Advanced word: **front**

behind him. All of a sud/den he felt warm inside—and very happy. A big smile came across his face.

"Yes, James, I do know who our teacher is," Brad said. "And you will like her a lot." Brad grinned at his mom. "She's my mom!" he said. God did hear him pray. He sent the best teacher!

---

behind

Sight word: **very**

Advanced word: **warm**

The Sunday School Secret

Which picture matches the sentence? Mark the ○ under the correct picture.

1. Brad got ready for Sunday school.

○　　　　　○　　　　　○

2. Beth heard Mom talking on the phone.

○　　　　　○　　　　　○

3. Brad and Beth rode home in the car.

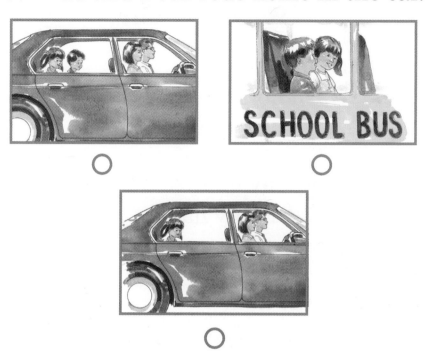

     ○   ○

     ○

4. Brad dropped a shoe on his toe.

   ○   ○   ○

Wash My Hair

Wash my hair,
   Wash my hair,
      Scrub, scrub, scrub.

Dry my hair,
   Dry my hair,
      Rub, rub, rub.

Comb my hair,
   Comb my hair;
      I'll sit still in my seat.

Be/cause tomorrow is
   Sunday school,
      And I want to be neat.

—*Laurel Hicks*

---

comb

Sight word: **tomorrow**   Advanced words: **hair** **be/cause**

Think and answer: What day will the next day be?

PART 3
Animal Adventures

Morning at the Zoo

Before they open up the gates
  To let the peo/ple in,
Do you suppose the animals
  Must dress up in their skins?
And if the zebra's zipper stuck
  And penguin lost his vest,
Do you suppose the zoo would
    close
  Till everyone was dressed?

—*Cheryl Parvin*

---

they   **zebra's**

Sight word: **penguin**   Advanced word: **would**

122

Ben Bug

Ben Bug went for a walk one day.

"I need to look for a home," he said.
"I need a place for Bonnie and me.
A wife needs a nice home. I want to
make a nice home for Bonnie."

He saw a hole up in a tree. "Is that
a nice place for a home? It looks nice
to me."

123

But just then
a big black bird flew
by. It went into
the hole.

"Oh, my, that must be his home!
I can't make my home in that spot.
That bird will eat Bonnie and me.
Oh, no! I had better go on."

He came to a big pond. He saw a
lil/y pad out in the water.

———
eat

"How nice," he said. "A home that will float. Bonnie might like a home like a boat."

But then—oh, my! A frog hopped by. Hop, hop. Splash, splash. Up went the lily pad. Down went the lily pad in the pond.

"Oh, dear! That will not do for a home. Bonnie and I will drown. Besides, that frog likes to eat bugs. This is no place for our home. I had better go on."

Soon he came to a big patch of grass.

"What is this I see? It looks like a little jug with a small hole in it. A frog cannot get inside, and a bird cannot get in. But it is just right for me to go in."

Ben went into the jug and looked around.

"This will make a big home. I think Bonnie will like it. We will be safe in this jug.

But now I need a bed, and I need a rug. I want to make it nice for Bonnie."

Ben went out of the jug. He looked and looked. Then he saw a big rag. It was a red sock.

———
saw

"Oh, this is a good rag. It is just what I need. It will make a nice rug in our home."

He had to pull and tug, but at last he had it in the jug.

"Oh, this is nice! I like it, and I think Bonnie will, too. But now I need a bed. How can I make a bed? I'll go and look for one."

Advanced word: **pull**

He went out of his home.

He had to look and look and look. He saw a matchbox, but it was too big.

"It will not go in the hole of the jug."

Then he saw a little lid. It was the cap from a bottle of pop.

"This will be good."

from

"Let's see if I can get it home."

So he had to pull and tug and pull and tug. He got it up to the hole of the jug.

"Will it fit?" Pull, pull, pull.

"Look! It fits!" The cap fell into the jug.

"I'll go get Bonnie now. She must see our home."

Think and answer:

1. Why do you think Ben is working so hard to make things nice for Bonnie?

2. Do our parents work hard for us, too?

He ran to get Bonnie.
But on the way, he
saw a big lid. It was
the lid from a jar
of jam. It had water
in it, and it
was close
to his
home.

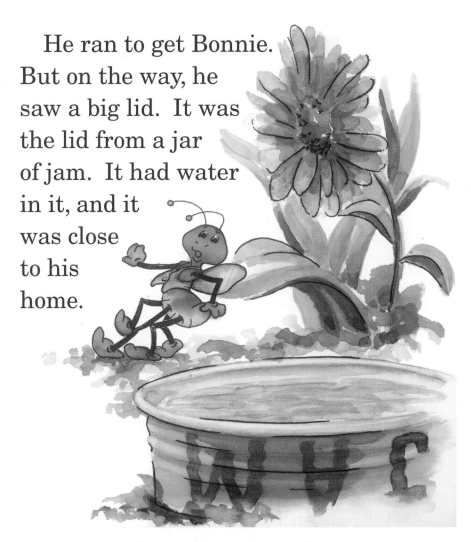

"That will make a fine place to
swim."

He climbed up a tall blade of grass.

"I can dive into the pool from this
spot. Here I go!"

Splash!

Off he went to
get Bonnie.

"Oh, Bonnie," he said, "You will like
our home."

"Tell me about it," Bonnie said.

"It is big and nice, and we will be
safe," Ben said.

Bonnie did like her home.

"I like to swim, and this pool is great," she cried. "And I like this nice red rug. But the bed—it is not good. How can we fix the bed? It is not soft."

Then she said, "Oh, Ben, I can make it soft."

She ran back to see her mom.

"Look at this, Ben," she said. "My mom had this cotton ball. It is soft."

Bonnie put it in the little lid.

great   cotton

Bonnie was right. It made a big soft bed for two little bugs.

"Get on the bed now. See how soft it is."

"It takes a wife to make a home nice," said Ben.

Think and answer:
1. What things did Ben do to make the home nice?
2. What things did Bonnie do?
3. Do you think Ben is thankful for what Bonnie did?
4. Do you think Bonnie is thankful for what Ben did?

First Things First

Number these pictures in the order that they took place in the story. Put 1 in the box under the picture that shows what happened first, then 2, then 3; and put 4 under the thing that happened last.

The Turkey

The turkey is a funny bird.
His head goes wobble, wobble.
All he says is just one word,
"Gobble, gobble,
     gobble!"

---

turkey   head

Sight word: **says**

Manners

Manners is
   to do and say
The nicest things
   in the
     nicest
      way.

---

nic/est

Rags

I have a dog, and his name is
    Rags.
He eats so much that his
    tummy sags.
His ears flip-flop, and his tail
    wig-wags.
And when he walks, he zigs
    and zags.

    Flip-flop
    Wiggle-waggle
    Zig-zag
        Flip-flop
        Wiggle-waggle
        Zig-zag

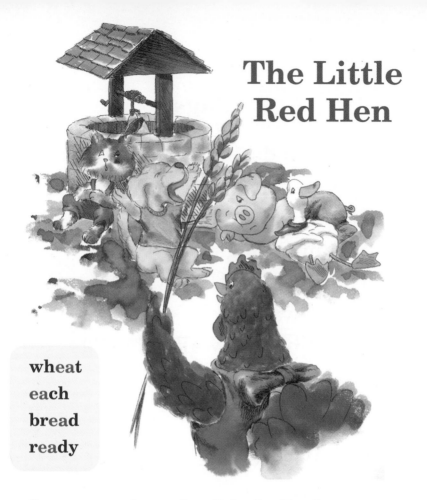

The Little Red Hen

wheat
each
bread
ready

One morning the Little Red Hen was scratching for food in the barnyard. She found a grain of wheat and called to her sleepy friends.

Little Red Hen: Who will help me plant this grain of wheat?

Sight word: **friends**

Her friends each opened one eye.

Dog: "Not I! I'm sleepy."
Cat: "Not I!"
Pig: "Not I!"
Duck: "Not I!"
Little Red Hen: "Then I will!"

And she planted the wheat in a corner of the barnyard. The wheat grew tall.

Soon it was ready to cut.

The Little Red Hen called to her friends. They were playing ball behind the barn.

Think and answer: What do you think will grow if you plant a grain of wheat?

Little Red Hen: "Who will help me cut the wheat?"

Dog: "Not I!"

Cat: "Not I! It's too hot!"

Pig: "Not I!"

Duck: "Not I!"

Little Red Hen: "Then I will!"

It was a hot job, but soon the Little Red Hen had cut all the wheat.

Little Red Hen: "Hm, the next step is to thresh the wheat."

Think and answer:
1. What do you think might be the real reason the Little Red Hen's friends won't help her?
2. Do you think the Little Red Hen is lazy?

"Threshing is hard work. I wish the dog or the pig would help me. They are stronger than I am. I will ask them."

The Little Red Hen found her friends sitting in the shade of the oak tree. They were hot after playing their ball game.

Little Red Hen: "Who will help me thresh the wheat?"

    Dog: "Not I!"
    Cat: "Not I!"
    Pig: "Not I! I'm tired."
    Duck: "Not I!"

They all sat drinking cold drinks.

Little Red Hen: "Then I will!"

It was hard work, and it took her a long time. Her friends were napping by the time she was done.

The next morning the Little Red Hen got up early. The wheat must go to the mill to be ground into flour. She looked at her sleeping friends.

_____
done

Little Red Hen: "Who will help me take the wheat to the mill?"

Her friends did not e/ven open their eyes.

Dog: "Not I!"
Cat: "Not I!"
Pig: "Not I!"
Duck: "Not I! Go away!"
They kept on sleeping.
Little Red Hen: "Then I will!"

She called all her chicks, and down the road they went to the mill.

When the Little Red Hen got back, her friends were heading for the swimming hole. Cat had a book to read.

Little Red Hen: "I'm glad I saw you! Now it's time to make the bread. Who will help me make the flour into bread?"

Dog: "Not I! It's too hot to cook!"

Cat: "Not I!"

Pig: "Not I!"

Duck: "Not I!"

heading   read   bread

So the Little Red Hen baked the bread and set the golden loaf on the table to cool.

Soon her friends came by on their way home from the swimming hole. They smelled the fresh bread.

Little Red Hen: "Who will help me eat this bread?"
Dog: "I will!"
Cat: "I will! It smells good."
Pig: "I will!"
Duck: "I will!"

But the Little Red Hen shook her head.

Little Red Hen: "You would not help me plant the wheat. You would not help me cut the wheat. You would not help me thresh the wheat or take it to the mill."

Little Red Hen: "You would not help me bake the bread, so you will not get to eat the bread. My chicks and I will eat it."

And they did!

🌱 Old Mother Hubbard

Old Mother Hubbard
    went to the cupboard,
To get her poor dog a bone.
But when she got there,
    the cupboard was bare,
And so the poor dog had none.

🌱 My Black Hen

Hick/e/ty, pick/e/ty, my black hen,
She lays eggs for gen/tle/men;
Sometimes nine and sometimes ten,
Hickety, pickety, my black hen.

🌱 Raining on the Farm

The hens lay eggs in the chicken coop,
The horses munch hay in the barn,
And the children play in the
    house today,
Because it's raining on
    the farm.

—*Laurel Hicks*

---

because

Sight words: **Hubbard** **cupboard**   Advanced word: **bare**

Who and What?

Mark the ○ under the picture that answers the question.

1. What did the Little Red Hen find in the barnyard?

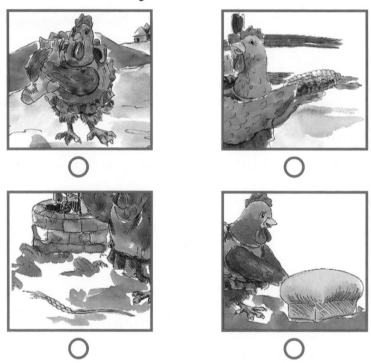

2. Who were the Little Red Hen's friends?

3. Who took the wheat to the mill?

○

○   ○

4. What did the Little Red Hen bake with the flour?

○   ○

○   ○

The Three Little Pigs

One day a mother pig called her three little pigs and talked to them sadly.

Mother Pig: "You are growing up now. It is time for you to go out on your own. Here is some money for each of you. It will help you get started.

Mother   some

150

Mother Pig: "Be good little pigs, and watch out for the big bad wolf!"

First Little Pig: "Thank you, Mother!"

Second Little Pig: "Thank you, Mother!"

Third Little Pig: "Thank you, Mother! We will try to be good, and we will watch out for the big bad wolf."

---

second

Sight word: **wolf**

151

The first two little pigs ran and skipped down the road. The third little pig was not so fast. He was looking all around for the big bad wolf. Soon the pigs came to a little town. The first little pig saw a man selling straw.

First Little Pig: "This is just what I need to build my house! Straw is cheap.

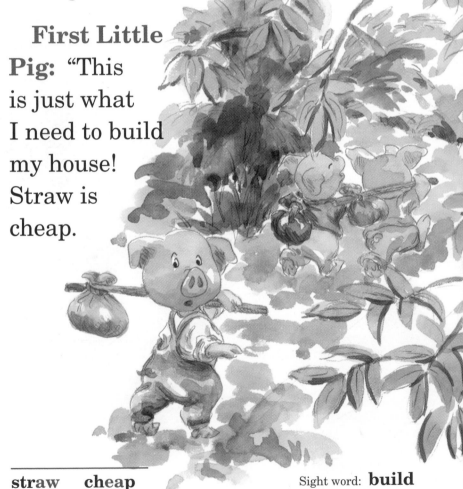

straw   cheap

Sight word: **build**

I can get all the straw I need and still have money left to get candy."

So the first little pig got lots of straw for his house. Then he got candy. But the house he built was not strong.

When the second little pig came into town, he saw a man selling sticks.

Sight word: **built**

Second Little Pig: "This is just what I need to build my house! A house built of sticks will not take much money. I will be a/ble to get a nice toy, too."

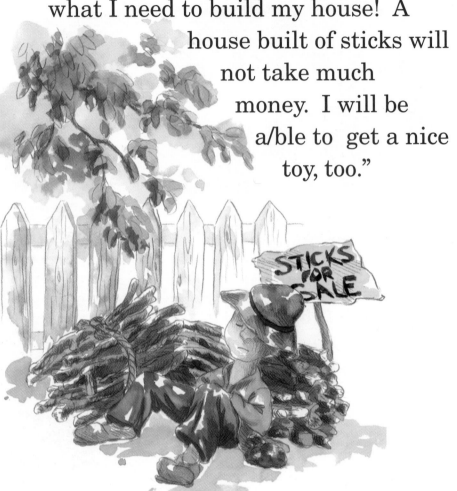

So the second little pig got a bundle of sticks to build his house. Then he got a game at the toy store. But the house he built was not sturdy.

When the third little pig came to town, he saw a man selling bricks.

Third Little Pig:
"This is just what I need to build my house. Bricks will make a strong house. It will keep me safe from the wolf."

So the third little pig got a load of bricks. It took him a long time to build his strong house.

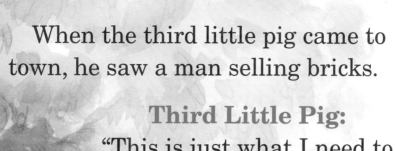

Think and answer: Which do you think this little pig is thinking more about, playing games or being safe?

It was not long before the wolf heard that the pigs had left home and had each built a house. He put on his best coat and hat and rushed out.

Soon he found the first little pig's house of straw. He knocked on the door and said in a high, sweet voice,

Wolf: "Little Pig, Little Pig, let me come in."

voice   come

Advanced word: **put**

The pig peeked out a hole in his house and saw the wolf!

First Little Pig: "Not by the hair of my chinny-chin-chin."

Wolf: "Then I'll huff, and I'll puff, and I'll blow your house in!"

The wolf got a big breath. Then he huffed, and he puffed, and he blew the straw house down.

———————

breath

Advanced word: **hair**

Meanwhile, the little pig ducked out the back and ran all the way to the second little pig's house.

First Little Pig: "Please let me in, dear Brother! The wolf came and blew my house down!"

The second little pig heard his brother's voice. He opened the door quickly and let him in.

___

please   brother

It did not take the wolf long to find
the house made of sticks. He put on
a big smile and then knocked on the
door.

Wolf: "Little Pig, Little Pig, please
let me come in." He spoke in that
same high, sweet voice.

But the second little pig peeked
out the window and knew it was the
wolf.

Second Little Pig: "Not by the hair of my chinny-chin-chin."

Wolf: "Then I'll huff, and I'll puff, and I'll blow your house in!"

The wolf got a big breath, and he huffed, and he puffed, and soon the house was just a pile of sticks on the ground. But the first and second little pigs had gotten out the back, and now they ran all the way to the third little pig's house.

They banged on the door of the brick house.

Second Little Pig: "Please let us in, dear Brother! The wolf has blown down our houses of straw and sticks. We need a strong house to hide in."

Think and answer: Do you think the first two brothers wished they had built a brick house, too?

The third little pig heard his brother's voice and opened the door. The pigs rushed in. He saw how scared they were. He started to tell them that they had been foolish to use part of their money on candy and toys, but he knew they had learned a good lesson.

lesson

Advanced word: **scared**

Third Little Pig: "Quick! Put the big kettle on to boil! The wolf will be here soon!"

It did not take the wolf long to find the house made of bricks. He walked round and round it. He saw the strong walls and the thick door.

He saw the big sturdy chimney.

chimney

He knew the third little pig had worked hard on his house.

The wolf put on his best smile and fixed his hat so that his ears did not show. He spoke in his sweetest voice.

Wolf: "Little Pig, Little Pig, let me come in. This is not the big, bad wolf. I've come to see your lovely house."

___
lovely

But the pigs had seen the wolf out the window. They had seen the big tail showing under the coat.

Third Little Pig: "Not by the hair of my chinny-chin-chin!"

Wolf: "Then I'll huff, and I'll puff, and I'll blow your house in."

The wolf huffed, and he puffed, but the house did not come down.

He took a bigger breath, and he huffed, and he puffed, and then he puffed, and he huffed, but still the house did not fall down. The wolf lay on the ground panting, all out of breath.

Then he looked up and saw the big chimney. He had a plan. He went around to the back of the house and climbed up on the roof.

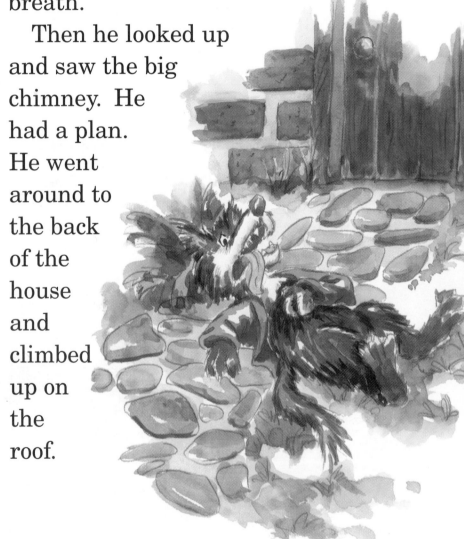

Wolf: "I'll get them yet! I'll come down the chimney."

Third Little Pig: "I hear him on the roof! I'll take the lid off the big kettle!"

The third little pig rushed to the pot. The water was boiling nicely.

Just then the wolf fell down the chimney right into the pot.

nicely

The smart little pig popped the lid on top of the kettle. His brothers cheered! That was the end of the big bad wolf!

From then on all three brothers stayed in the brick house. They watched out for wolves, and they spent money wisely.

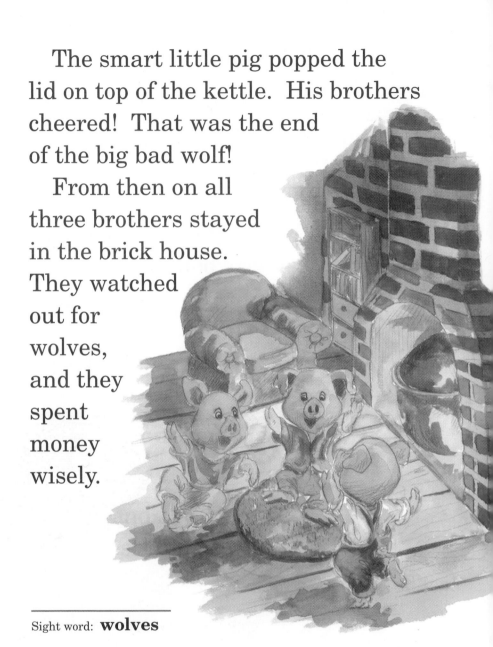

Sight word: **wolves**

Think and answer:
1. What advice did the mother pig give her sons?
2. Was it good advice?
3. Why should we listen to our mothers?

Which Words?

Look at the pictures below. There are two rows of words to go with each one. One word in each row will remind you of the animal in the picture. Mark the ○ under those words.

sticks	straw	bricks
○	○	○
work	toy	candy
○	○	○

sticks	straw	bricks
○	○	○
work	toy	candy
○	○	○

sticks	straw	bricks
○	○	○
work	toy	candy
○	○	○

Fuzzy Wuzzy

Fuzzy Wuzzy was
a bear.
Fuzzy Wuzzy had
no hair.
Then Fuzzy Wuzzy
wasn't fuzzy,
was he?

Alexander Alligator

Al/ex/an/der Al/li/ga/tor
wears a happy grin
Starting at his earholes
and reaching to his chin.

—*Laurel Hicks*

Bow-wow,
Says the Dog

Bow-wow, says the dog;
Mew, mew, says the cat;
Oink, oink, says the hog;
And squeak, says the rat.

To who? says the owl;
Caw, caw, says the crow;
Quack, quack, says the duck;
And moo, says the cow.

---

squeak   caw

Animal Alphabet

A was an ant
Who seldom stood still,
And who made a nice house
In the side of a hill.

　　a

　　Nice little ant!

—Edward Lear

B was a bat
Who slept all the day,
And fluttered about
When the sun went away.

　　b

　　Brown little bat!

—Edward Lear

C was a camel:
You rode on his hump;
And if you fell off,
You came down such a
bump!

c

What a high camel!

—*Edward Lear*

D was a duck
With spots on his back,
Who lived in the water,
And always said, "Quack!"

d

Dear little duck!

—*Edward Lear*

Sight word: **lived**   Advanced word: **always**

E was an elephant,
Stately and wise;
He had tusks and a trunk,
And two odd little eyes.

e

Oh, what funny small
eyes!

—*Edward Lear*

F was a fox
As sly as could be.
He watched the fat mouse
From behind the oak tree.

f

Crafty old fox!

—*Marion Hedquist*

Advanced word: **could**

G was a goat
Who was
     spotted with
     brown;
When he did not
     lie still
He walked up and down.

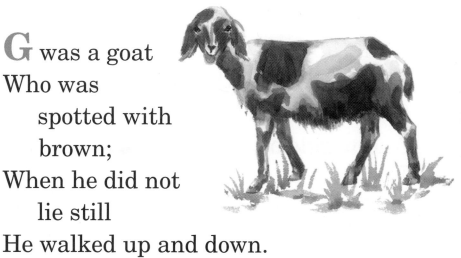

g
     Good little goat!

—*Edward Lear*

H was a horse
With a long flowing mane.
     He ran like the wind
     Across the wide plain.
     h
     Fast running horse!

—*Marion Hedquist*

I was an inchworm
Bright green on the ground.
See him hunch his back
And wiggle off to town.
    i
    Clever inchworm!

—*Marion Hedquist*

J was a jaguar
High up in the tree
With shiny green eyes
Peering down at me.
    j
    Sleek spotted jaguar!

—*Marion Hedquist*

Sight word: **jaguar**

K was a kingfisher;
Quickly he flew—
So bright and so pretty!—
Green, purple, and blue.
   k
   Kingfisher blue!

—Edward Lear

L was a lion,
A very large cat.
Sleeping in the sunshine and
Getting old and fat.
  l

  Majestic lion!

—Marion Hedquist

Think and answer: What do you suppose a kingfisher eats?

M was a monkey
Swinging in
   the tree.
Just for a joke
He might land
    on me!
  m
   Funny little monkey!

      —Marion Hedquist

N was a night owl
Sleeping all day
   long.
He gets up at bedtime
And starts to sing his
    song.
  n
   Who-o-o-Owl-Who!

      —Marion Hedquist

monkey

O was an ostrich;
He was very tall;
He stood on two legs,
And never did fall.

    o

    Awe/some ostrich!

—*Judy Hazewinkel*

P was a pig
Who was not very big;
But his tail was too curly,
And that made him surly.

    p

    Cross little pig!

—*Edward Lear*

Awe/some

Q was a quail
With a very short tail,
And he fed upon corn
In the evening
and morn.
q
Quaint little quail!

—*Edward Lear*

R was a rabbit,
Who had a bad habit
Of eating the flowers
In gardens and bowers.
r
Naughty, fat rabbit!

—*Edward Lear*

---
naughty

S was a seal
Who lived in the zoo.
He liked to eat fish
And play ball with you.

s

Cute little seal!

—*Marion Hedquist*

T was a turtle
Hiding in his shell.
If he has a name,
He will never tell.

t

Shy little turtle!

—*Laurel Hicks*

U was an um/brel/la bird
With a long feath/ered vest
And over his head
He can spread out his crest!

u

Beautiful umbrella
bird!

—*Marion Hedquist*

V was a vul/ture.
See his big feet?
They clutch his supper
Till he's ready to eat!

v

Hun/gry vulture!

—*Marion Hedquist*

---

umbrella   **feathered**   **spread**

Sight word: **beautiful**   Advanced word: **vulture**

182

W was a woodpecker.
See that round hole?
He made it with his beak
In the telephone pole.

w

Noisy Woodpecker!

—*Marion Hedquist*

X was an ox.
Farmer Brown calls him
"Jack."
He can carry any load
On his strong, wide back.

x

Helpful old ox!

—*Marion Hedquist*

Advanced words: **carry   helpful**

Y was a yak,
From the land
of Ti/bet.
Except his white tail,
He was all black as jet.

y
Look at the yak!

—Edward Lear

Z was a zebra,
All striped white and
black;
And if he were tame
You might ride
on his back.

z
Pretty striped zebra!

—Edward Lear

Think and answer:
1. Name all of the birds in the animal alphabet.
2. Which animals would you find in a zoo?
3. Which animals would you find on a farm?

Contraction Contest

Can you match each contraction with the correct two words? Draw lines to connect the ones that match.

can't	I will
I'll	let us
let's	I am
I'm	can not

See if you can match these contractions.

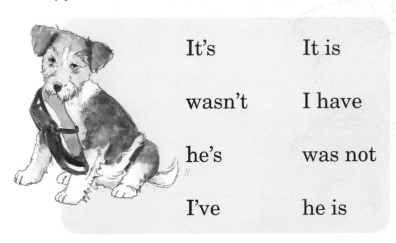

It's	It is
wasn't	I have
he's	was not
I've	he is

I Love to Read!

I love to read
  about
    Places to go and
      things to do,

Animals that live
  at the farm or the zoo.

Twins that learn on
  God to depend,

But now, it's time
  to say:

The End.

—*M. Hedquist*